Electronic Keyboard Grade 2

Pieces & Technical Work
for Trinity Guildhall examinations

2011-2013

Published by
Trinity College London
89 Albert Embankment
London SE1 7TP UK

T +44 (0)20 7820 6100
F +44 (0)20 7820 6161
E music@trinityguildhall.co.uk
www.trinityguildhall.co.uk

Printed in England by Halstan & Co. Ltd, Amersham, Bucks.

Minuet

from Quintet op. 13 no. 5

Luigi Boccherini
arr. Natalie Bleicher

Voices: Harp/Flute (dual voice Harp)
Style: Waltz

PLEASE SET UP FOR THE NEXT PIECE

Own Interpretation

Mozartian Melody

from Symphony no. 39

Wolfgang Amadeus Mozart
arr. Keith Beniston

Voices: _____

Style: _____

The repeat must be played in the examination.

PLEASE SET UP FOR THE NEXT PIECE

Chopin Odyssey

Frédéric Chopin
arr. Nancy Litten

Voices: Oboe/Strings
Style: Waltz (not Viennese)

PLEASE SET UP FOR THE NEXT PIECE

This piece is published under licence from Nancy Litten.

Danny Boy

Traditional
arr. Victoria Proudler

Voices: Pan Flute (dual voice Strings)
Style: Ballad

PLEASE SET UP FOR THE NEXT PIECE

The House of the Rising Sun

Traditional
arr. Joanna Clarke

Voices: Jazz Guitar/Strings
Style: 6/8 Ballad

PLEASE SET UP FOR THE NEXT PIECE

Improvisation

La Cumparsita

Voices: Alto Saxophone/Strings
Style: Tango

Gerardo Matos Rodríguez
arr. Nancy Litten

PLEASE SET UP FOR THE NEXT PIECE

Dance Etude

Victoria Proudler

PLEASE SET UP FOR THE NEXT PIECE

Hallelujah

Leonard Cohen
arr. Victoria Proudler

Voices: Flute/Strings
Style: ⁶⁄₈ Slow Rock

PLEASE SET UP FOR THE NEXT PIECE

Haunted House

Lindsey Butterfield

Voices: Vibes/Saxophone
Style: Swing

Creeping along ♩ = 120

Look around for ghosts ...

* Play as a chord cluster − as many black and white notes as you can −
with the whole of the right hand flat on the keys.

PLEASE SET UP FOR THE NEXT PIECE

Bhajan

Traditional
arr. Jyotishka Dasgupta

Voices: Sitar*(or 12 String Guitar if Sitar not available)/Flute
Style: Bhajan (or 8 Beat Pop if Bhajan not available)

* sounding one octave lower (use of pitch bend permitted).

PLEASE SET UP FOR THE NEXT PIECE

Technical Work

All sections i) to iii) to be prepared. Sections i) and ii) must be performed from memory; the music may be used for Section iii).

i) Scales

The following scales to be performed in piano voice with auto-accompaniment off, hands together (unless otherwise stated), ♩ = 80, *legato* and **mf**:

 B♭ and D major (two octaves)
 G and B minor (two octaves): candidate's choice of *either* harmonic *or* melodic *or* natural minor
 Chromatic scale in similar motion starting on B♭ (one octave)
 Pentatonic scale starting on B♭ and D, hands separately (one octave)

B♭ major scale (two octaves)

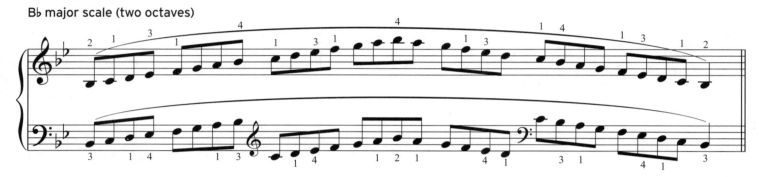

D major scale (two octaves)

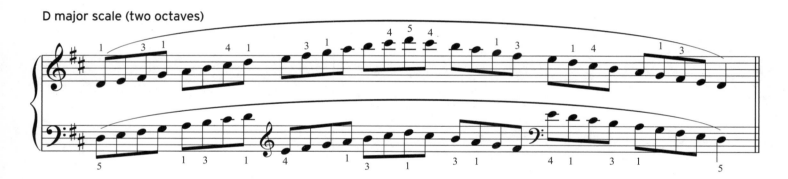

G minor scale: harmonic (two octaves)

G minor scale: melodic (two octaves)

G minor scale: natural (two octaves)

B minor scale: harmonic (two octaves)

B minor scale: melodic (two octaves)

B minor scale: natural (two octaves)

Chromatic scale in similar motion starting on B♭ (one octave)

Pentatonic scale starting on B♭ (one octave)

Right hand

Left hand

Pentatonic scale starting on D (one octave)

Right hand

Left hand

ii) Chord knowledge

The following to be performed with the left hand in piano voice with auto-accompaniment off:

Triad of B♭ and D major, G and B minor (root position, first and second inversions)
Chord of B♭^{7} and D^7 (root position, first and second inversions)

B♭ major

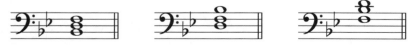

D major

G minor

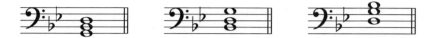

B minor

Bb⁷

D⁷

iii) Exercises

Candidate to prepare all three exercises.

1. Medieval Mood – bass clef reading and finger dexterity

Voice: Piano (dual voice Strings)
Style: Ballad

Accomp. off
Rhythm on

Smoothly [♩ = c. 80]

2. Mountain Pass – arpeggios and chord use [fingered chords must be used]

Voice: Flute
Style: ⁶⁄₈ Ballad

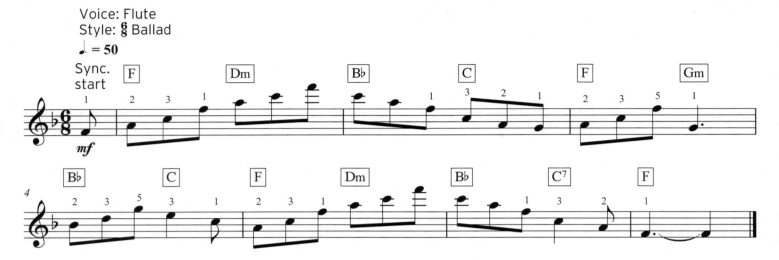

3. Twistin' Tango – using keyboard functions

Voice: Violin
Style: Tango

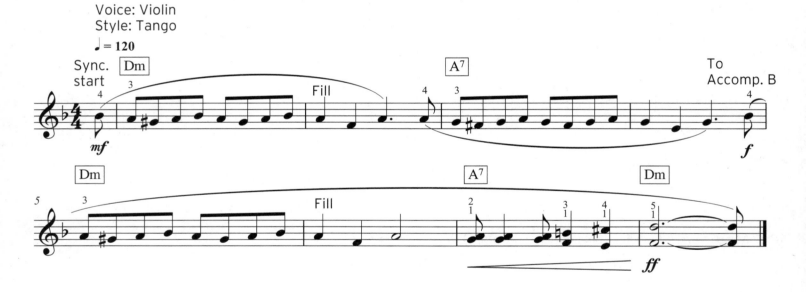